The Little One

The Story of a Red-Tailed Monkey

First published in 2009
This edition published 2010 by

black dog books

15 Gertrude Street
Fitzroy Vic 3065
Australia
61 + 3 + 9419 9406
61 + 3 + 9419 1214 (fax)
dog@bdb.com.au

For Sachi Oda Mojarrabi—a wonderful friend!

Designed by Guy Holt Design
Printed and bound in China by 1010 Printing International

ISBN: 9781742031224 (pbk)

P16: With special thanks to Dr Richard Ssuna and Debby Cox.
All photographs taken by Dr Carla Litchfield

10 9 8 7 6 5 4 3 2 1   10 11 12 13

The Little One

The Story of a Red-Tailed Monkey

By Kaitie Afrika Litchfield

My name is Kaitie. I live in Adelaide, Australia.
When I was four years old, my mom and
I lived in Uganda in Africa. She is a scientist, and
she was working at a sanctuary for orphaned
chimpanzees. Her job was to find out how
chimps solve puzzles.

Uganda is sometimes called the 'Pearl of Africa' because it is so beautiful. It has volcanoes, rainforests, and huge Lake Victoria. It is also where the River Nile starts its journey to Egypt. Uganda has gorillas, chimpanzees, elephants, lions, giraffes, and lots of monkeys. Everywhere we went, the people were friendly and kind.

I went to Kissyfur Nursery School in Entebbe until just after lunch every day. We would read, draw, sing and dance, and we spent a lot of time practicing for the Christmas concert. I loved lunchtime because we had beans and rice, sugar bananas, and chapattis which are small, salty pancakes. The food was delicious!

Sometimes after school I would meet my friends at the Wildlife Education Centre, and we would visit the chimps. We would ride the donkeys, walk to the lake, or pretend to be different animals.

One day, my life changed. Some people arrived with a baby red-tailed monkey. He was tiny and quiet and scared. A farmer had killed his mom because she was stealing his crops.

The farmer had tried to sell the baby monkey.
This was against the law, so the monkey was
brought to us. The adults in the house were busy
looking after the chimpanzees, so I became the
little monkey's mom.

The first day, I didn't know what to do. He was
tiny and I didn't want to accidentally hurt him.
But I didn't need to worry because, once he
climbed onto me, he wouldn't let go.

After I gave him a drink of milk we both felt more comfortable. I decided to call him The Little One which annoyed the adults who all wanted to call him something else! But I was his mom, and that was his name.

Every day, before I went to nursery school in Entebbe, The Little One and I had breakfast together. The Little One ate banana, apple, pineapple, mango, and passionfruit. I had the same, and also cereal and bread.

When he got older, The Little One stole food from our plates. The adults in the house didn't like that at all, but I thought it was funny!

Like all babies, The Little One needed milk to grow big and strong. Every night I gave him milk. My mom and the others in the house gave him his milk when I was at school.

In the wild, red-tailed monkeys groom each other. Every day I would groom The Little One. I would gently pick through his hair while he relaxed. It was fun, and he enjoyed it too!

The Little One thought I was his mom, and never liked to be far away from me. He snuffled my ear and ran all over me.

When he put his velvety hands and feet on me,
it tickled and made me giggle. Playing together
made us both happy.

When he first came to us, The Little One needed
to have a health check. While The Little One was
asleep the vet weighed and measured him, and
also took a copy of his handprint.

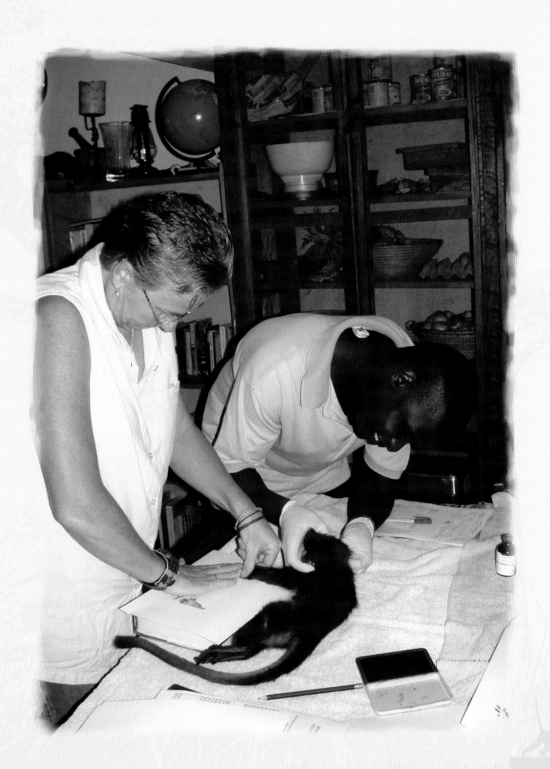

The Little One loved riding on Millie Dog and Monty Dog. The dogs loved The Little One, even when he bounced on their bellies and hugged them and was very annoying!

We had a homeless puppy staying for a few days, and she loved playing. The Little One would climb up a pole and jump on the puppy, then roll around with her on the ground.

Dewar the cat was not very cuddly with people, but he was good friends with The Little One. He even let the little monkey ride around on his back! They pulled at each other's tail, and chased one another around the house.

The Little One shared all my toys. He loved
holding the soft and cuddly unicorn. Sometimes
I carried them both around.

The Little One loved playing
under my hat. He hid under
it when he was scared, and
played hide-and-seek in it
when he was happy.
He fitted inside it perfectly,
so sometimes I would walk
around with him sitting on my head!

The Little One needed to come with us on short trips. Sometimes he made scared sounds and hugged me really tight. But I made him feel safe when I patted him and told him not to worry.

On wash day, The Little One and I had the most fun. We hid in the washing basket, and when I pushed off the lid, out came The Little One, like a jack-in-the-box! Then he would climb back in and start over again.

The Little One loved water. While the adults washed clothes, we would jump in and out of the washtubs. We drove the adults crazy! He loved water so much that while I was taking a bath, he would leap in and swim laps.

Then he would sleep in the basket on top of all the soft clothes.

In Uganda it is against the law to keep monkeys as pets. So when The Little One was old enough to look after himself, my job as his mom was over. He couldn't go back to the wild because he loved people too much, and might not have had the skills to survive.

So The Little One went to live with a little
female red-tailed monkey at the Uganda Wildlife
Education Centre, just down the road from our
house. I took him to his new home to settle him
in. One of the saddest days of my life was the day
I said goodbye to The Little One.

Information on red-tailed monkeys:

Red-tailed monkeys are found in the Democratic Republic of Congo, Rwanda, Uganda, Kenya and Tanzania. They can be recognized by the bright white spot on their nose, white cheek hair, and long red tail.

When red-tailed monkeys greet a friend, they touch noses and play with or groom each other. Youngsters make soft trilling sounds when an older monkey approaches to show they know who is boss. Red-tailed monkeys are **diurnal**, which means that they sleep at night and are active during the day. They are also mainly **arboreal** which means they spend most of their time in the trees.

The Little One was born in the forest at Kibale National Park where red-tailed monkeys live alongside blue monkeys, red colobus monkeys and other types of monkeys. Scientists here noticed that other monkeys like to be near red-tailed monkeys because red-tailed monkeys are really good at spotting predators. If they see a dangerous animal like a crowned-hawk eagle in the sky, the red-tailed monkeys make alarm calls to warn everyone to be careful.

Unfortunately, forests are being cut down, and farmers sometimes plant crops right next to the remaining forest. If there is not enough fruit in the forest, or if monkeys decide they like the taste of sugarcane, bananas or other yummy crops, they will start taking food. Farmers try to chase them away, or even kill them. Red-tailed monkeys are clever, so some have learned to wait until night to raid crops. They have cheek pouches which means they can cram food into their cheeks then run back to the forest and eat the food slowly. Even though red-tailed monkeys are not endangered, they suffer because of the problems caused by the destruction of their habitats.